The Snow and the Sun

La Nieve y el Sol

ALSO BY ANTONIO FRASCONI

SEE AND SAY:
A Picture Book in Four Languages

THE HOUSE THAT JACK BUILT:
A Picture Book in Two Languages

A South American Folk Rhyme in Two Languages

THE SNOW AND THE SUN

LA NIEVE Y EL SOL

Woodcuts by Antonio Frasconi

Harcourt, Brace & World, Inc., New York

This rhyme is my own translation and version of one published by the Education Council of Argentina in a textbook for primary schools. I remember in my childhood in Montevideo, Uruguay, that we had a story in our reader that was similar in theme to this rhyme. In reading it, we learned not only the sound and meaning of the words, but a lesson in life as well, that everything in nature is closely related to the things around it; that each action produces a reaction. An interesting aspect of this rhyme is its similarity to some of the old folk tales of other countries. The opening line in the rhyme, "Snow that hurts my feet," may reveal something about its origin, for in all Uruguay and most of Argentina snow is unknown.

A.F.

Snow that hurts my feet,
why are you bad?
I am not bad;
the Sun is bad
that melts me.

Nieve que lastimas mis pies,
¿por qué eres mala?
Yo no soy mala;
el Sol es malo
me derrite a mí.

Sun that melts the snow,
Snow that hurts my feet,
why are you bad?
I am not bad;
the Cloud is bad
that covers me.

Sol que derrites la nieve,
Nieve que lastimas mis pies,
¿por qué eres malo?
Yo no soy malo;
la Nube es mala
que me oculta a mí.

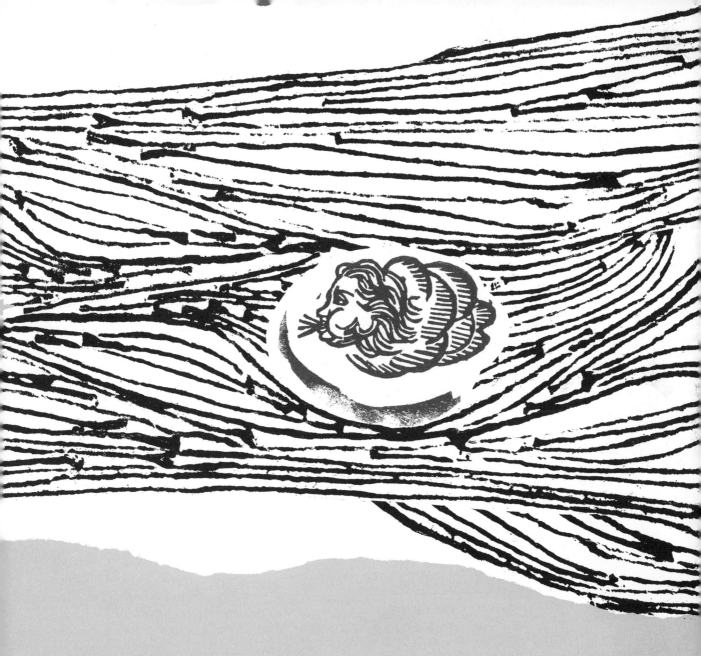

Cloud that covers the sun,
Sun that melts the snow,
Snow that hurts my feet,
why are you bad?
I am not bad;
the Wind is bad
that blows me away.

Nube que ocultas el sol,
Sol que derrites la nieve,
Nieve que lastimas mis pies,
¿por qué eres mala?
Yo no soy mala;
el Viento es malo,
que me lleva a mi.

Wind that blows away the cloud,
Cloud that covers the sun,
Sun that melts the snow,
Snow that hurts my feet,
why are you bad?
I am not bad;
the Wall is bad
that stops me.

Viento que llevas la nube,
Nube que ocultas el sol,
Sol que derrites la nieve,
Nieve que lastimas mis pies,
¿por qué eres malo?
Yo no soy malo;
la Pared es mala
que me ataja a mí.

Wall that stops the wind,
Wind that blows away the cloud,
Cloud that covers the sun,
Sun that melts the snow,
Snow that hurts my feet,
why are you bad?
I am not bad;
the Rat is bad
that digs under me.

Pared que atajas el viento,
Viento que llevas la nube,
Nube que ocultas el sol,
Sol que derrites la nieve,
Nieve que lastimas mis pies,
¿por qué eres mala?
Yo no soy mala;
mala es la Rata
que me cava a mí.

Rat that digs under the wall,
Wall that stops the wind,
Wind that blows away the cloud,
Cloud that covers the sun,
Sun that melts the snow,

Snow that hurts my feet,
why are you bad?
I am not bad;
the Cat is bad
that chases me.

Rata que cavas la pared,
Pared que atajas el viento,
Viento que llevas la nube,
Nube que ocultas el sol,
Sol que derrites la nieve,

Nieve que lastimas mis pies,
¿por qué eres mala?
Yo no soy mala;
malo es el Gato
que me acosa a mí.

Cat that chases the rat,
Rat that digs under the wall,
Wall that stops the wind,
Wind that blows away the cloud,
Cloud that covers the sun,
Sun that melts the snow,
Snow that hurts my feet,
why are you bad?
I am not bad;
the Dog is bad
that barks at me.

Gato que acosas la rata,
Rata que cavas la pared,
Pared que atajas el viento,
Viento que llevas la nube,
Nube que ocultas el sol,
Sol que derrites la nieve,
Nieve que lastimas mis pies,
¿por qué eres malo?
Yo no soy malo;
malo es el Perro
que me ladra a mí.

Dog that barks at the cat,
Cat that chases the rat,
Rat that digs under the wall,
Wall that stops the wind,
Wind that blows away the cloud,
Cloud that covers the sun,
Sun that melts the snow,
Snow that hurts my feet,
why are you bad?
I am not bad;
the Stick is bad
that beats me.

Perro que ladras al gato,
Gato que acosas la rata,
Rata que cavas la pared,
Pared que atajas el viento,
Viento que llevas la nube,
Nube que ocultas el sol,
Sol que derrites la nieve,
Nieve que lastimas mis pies,
¿por qué eres malo?
Yo no soy malo;
malo es el Palo
que me pega a mí.

Stick that beats the dog,
Dog that barks at the cat,
Cat that chases the rat,
Rat that digs under the wall,
Wall that stops the wind,
Wind that blows away the cloud,
Cloud that covers the sun,
Sun that melts the snow,
Snow that hurts my feet,
why are you bad?
I am not bad;
the Fire is bad
that burns me.

Palo que pegas al perro,
Perro que ladras al gato,
Gato que acosas la rata,
Rata que cavas la pared,
Pared que atajas el viento,
Viento que llevas la nube,
Nube que ocultas el sol,
Sol que derrites la nieve,
Nieve que lastimas mis pies,
¿por qué eres malo?
Yo no soy malo;
malo es el Fuego
que me quema a mí.

Fire that burns the stick,
Stick that beats the dog,
Dog that barks at the cat,
Cat that chases the rat,
Rat that digs under the wall,
Wall that stops the wind,
Wind that blows away the cloud,
Cloud that covers the sun,
Sun that melts the snow,
Snow that hurts my feet,
why are you bad?
I am not bad;
the Water is bad
that quenches me.

Fuego que quemas el palo,
Palo que pegas al perro,
Perro que ladras al gato,
Gato que acosas la rata,
Rata que cavas la pared,
Pared que atajas el viento,
Viento que llevas la nube,
Nube que ocultas el sol,
Sol que derrites la nieve,
Nieve que lastimas mis pies,
¿por qué eres malo?
Yo no soy malo;
el Agua es mala
que me apaga a mí.

Water that quenches the fire,
Fire that burns the stick,
Stick that beats the dog,
Dog that barks at the cat,
Cat that chases the rat,
Rat that digs under the wall,
Wall that stops the wind,
Wind that blows away the cloud,
Cloud that covers the sun,
Sun that melts the snow,
Snow that hurts my feet,
why are you bad?
I am not bad;
the Ox is bad
that drinks me.

Agua que apagas el fuego,
Fuego que quemas el palo,
Palo que pegas al perro,
Perro que ladras al gato,
Gato que acosas la rata,
Rata que cavas la pared,
Pared que atajas el viento,
Viento que llevas la nube,
Nube que ocultas el sol,
Sol que derrites la nieve,
Nieve que lastimas mis pies,
¿por qué eres malo?
Yo no soy malo;
el Buey es malo
que me bebe a mí.

Ox that drinks the water,
Water that quenches the fire,
Fire that burns the stick,
Stick that beats the dog,
Dog that barks at the cat,
Cat that chases the rat,
Rat that digs under the wall,
Wall that stops the wind,
Wind that blows away the cloud,
Cloud that covers the sun,
Sun that melts the snow,
Snow that hurts my feet,
why are you bad?
I am not bad;
the Man is bad
that corrals me.

Buey que bebes el agua,
Agua que apagas el fuego,
Fuego que quemas el palo,
Palo que pegas al perro,
Perro que ladras al gato,
Gato que acosas la rata,
Rata que cavas la pared,
Pared que atajas el viento,
Viento que llevas la nube,
Nube que ocultas el sol,
Sol que derrites la nieve,
Nieve que lastimas mis pies,
¿por qué eres malo?
Yo no soy malo;
malo es el Hombre
que me encorrala a mí.

Cop.5

Man that corrals the ox,
Ox that drinks the water,
Water that quenches the fire,
Fire that burns the stick,
Stick that beats the dog,
Dog that barks at the cat,
Cat that chases the rat,
Rat that digs under the wall,
Wall that stops the wind,
Wind that blows away the cloud,
Cloud that covers the sun,
Sun that melts the snow,
Snow that hurts my feet,
why are you bad?

Hombre que encorralas al buey,
Buey que bebes el agua,
Agua que apagas el fuego,
Fuego que quemas el palo,
Palo que pegas al perro,
Perro que ladras al gato,
Gato que acosas la rata,
Rata que cavas la pared,
Pared que atajas el viento,
Viento que llevas la nube,
Nube que ocultas el sol,
Sol que derrites la nieve,
Nieve que lastimas mis pies,
¿por qué eres malo?

I am not bad;
the Snow is bad
that hurts my feet.

Yo no soy malo;
mala es la Nieve
que lastima mis pies.